Up-To-the-Minute Learning™
with
NATURAL DISASTERS

by Julie B. Froman

TABLE OF CONTENTS

TORNADOES

HURRICANES

INTRODUCTION

How many times do your students come in the door talking about something that is happening in their lives? They're talking about a tornado that touched ground not far away, the World Series, an earthquake that rocked Los Angeles, or an upcoming holiday.

Now is the time to jump on a topic that interests your students! **Teachable moments** happen when something of relevance to your students becomes the curriculum.

The activities in this book can be used to supplement your curriculum, or they can *become* your curriculum. They are divided into three sections: Earthquakes, Tornadoes, and Hurricanes.

The activities are designed to be used with minimal preparation time. They are ready to go the moment an earthquake, tornado, or hurricane happens. Each student should receive a copy of the Data Sheet, History Sheet, and Glossary. If a student activity requires materials, these materials will be listed in the "You Will Need" section on that page. For your convenience, each activity is matched with one general Curricular Area; some activities cover topics in more than one Curricular Area.

Each unit includes a bibliography of related children's books for Whole Language instruction.

Whether you use a few activities or the whole book, we hope that this book makes it easier to explore your curriculum in a way that is relevant, interesting, and fun for you and your students.

SOURCES OF FURTHER INFORMATION ON NATURAL DISASTERS:

- Local Newspapers
- Television Weather Forecasts
- Cable TV, Weather Channel

- The National Hurricane Center
  11691 Southwest 17th Street
  Miami, FL 33165
  1-305-229-4470

- The American Red Cross
  43 E. Ohio Street
  Chicago, IL 60611
  1-800-746-5463

TEACHING NOTES
Earthquakes

The Earthquake Unit is designed to be ready to go! When an earthquake happens, reproduce enough copies for your class, and do the activities together. Most activity sheets ask students first to fill in the name of the earthquake you are studying.

Here are some suggestions to make the most of your curriculum:

- Have students bring in newspaper or magazine articles on the earthquake you are studying to share them with the rest of the class.

- Collect periodical clippings, an atlas, a globe, maps, library books, and the projects your students complete in one area of your classroom. Call it the **Earthquake Information Center.**

- The activity pages are arranged in an order that seems to "flow" well. However, feel free to use the pages in a different order depending on your curricular needs.

- The table below outlines each activity with a general curricular area and the topics covered. Some activities cover topics from more than one curricular area.

Selected answers:
page 11: 1. 10 seconds, 10 seconds **3.** 4.25 seconds, 8.5 seconds, 8.5 seconds
page 13: 1. Alaska, 30 **3.** 900

DATA

Name _____

EARTHQUAKE DATA SHEET

LOCATION:

Record anything you know about the town or city nearest the epicenter below:

1. _____

_____

2. _____

_____

3. _____

_____

4. _____

_____

5. _____

_____

6. _____

_____

Most earthquakes are given the name of the city or town closest to the epicenter.

The earthquake you are studying has been named the _____ Earthquake.

Date of earthquake: _____ Richter Scale reading: _____

DAMAGE:

How many people were killed?

_____

How many people were left homeless?

_____

How many homes were destroyed?

_____

What is the financial estimate of the damage?

_____

Record any information about aftershocks below, with the date(s) they occurred:

Date	Effects (if any)
_____	_____
_____	_____
_____	_____
_____	_____

ADDITIONAL INFORMATION:

Record any additional information or observations in the space to the right. Use the back of this sheet if necessary.

_____

_____

_____

_____

Name _____

KWL

KWL

K —What I already <u>K</u>now   **W** — What I <u>W</u>ant to know
      L — What I have <u>L</u>earned

KWL is a tool that scientists use to investigate. You can do a KWL as you investigate this earthquake.

First, write down everything you already know about this earthquake. Where and when did it happen? What do you know about this place? What kind of damage did it cause, and what happened to the people near it? Don't worry if you are right or wrong. You will be checking your facts later.

WHAT I ALREADY KNOW:

1. _____
2. _____
3. _____
4. _____
5. _____
6. _____
7. _____

Now, write down anything you want to know about this earthquake. What questions do you have about this earthquake? How strong was it? What was the location like before the earthquake? How many buildings were damaged? Write down any questions that come to mind.

WHAT I WANT TO KNOW:

1. _____
2. _____
3. _____
4. _____
5. _____
6. _____
7. _____

WHAT I HAVE LEARNED:

As you learn more about this earthquake, you will complete the "L" part of the KWL. "L" stands for what you have learned. When you learn something new or answer one of your questions, write it down on the back of this sheet.

Name _____

EARTHQUAKE REPORTING

A newspaper **lead** (the first sentence or paragraph) tells the facts briefly and completely. Read the lead from a story on the _____ Earthquake. List the facts below in the 5 W's and H format:

"Who, What, When, Where, Why" are the 5 W's. "How" is the H.

<u>W</u>hat happened? _____

_____

<u>W</u>ho did it affect? _____

_____

<u>W</u>hen did it happen? _____

_____

<u>W</u>here did it happen? _____

_____

<u>W</u>hy did it happen? _____

_____

<u>H</u>ow did it happen? _____

_____

Write a lead for this earthquake using the above information, but saying it in your own way.

_____

_____

_____

Ancient Greeks once thought the Earth was carried on the back of the god Atlas. Use the 5W's and H provided below to write another lead and headline.

Who? The god Atlas
What? Shrugged his shoulders, causing an earthquake
When? Dusk of the current day (you supply the date)
Where? The planet Earth
Why? He was responding to the question, "What do you want on your hamburger?"
How? With a lift of his shoulders and a tilt of his head

Headline for story:

_____

Lead: _____

_____

_____

_____

_____

Name _____

WAVES THAT DESTROY

Earthquake waves can travel as fast as 16,000 mph (25,000 kph). That's fast! Sometimes if the earthquakes run through mud or sand, they do slow down.

Earthquake waves come in three stages:

p-waves, short for <u>p</u>rimary waves, which are the first to hit

s-waves, short for <u>s</u>econdary waves, which are the next to hit

l-waves, short for <u>l</u>arge waves (also called surface waves), are the last to hit

These three waves cause specific types of damage:

1. P-waves are felt by people and animals, and may ring church bells or cause small waves on the surface of ponds. The first waves, or p-waves, felt in the _____ Earthquake had the following effect on people:

_____

_____

_____

2. S-waves rock the ground from side to side, and can be some of the most destructive waves in an earthquake. Buildings shake until they crack or collapse, the ground seems to ripple up and down, and it is difficult to drive a car. The s-waves in the _____ Earthquake did the following damage:

_____

_____

Draw a sketch of some of the s-wave damage:

[   ]

3. L-waves bounce up and down, uprooting trees and causing landslides. These waves are sometimes called surface waves or large waves. The l-waves in the _____ Earthquake did the following damage:

_____

_____

_____

Draw a sketch of some of the l-wave damage:

[   ]

(If you are not sure whether s-waves or l-waves did the damage, the s-waves probably were responsible for some of the worst damage.)

WRITING

Name _____

ALL SHOOK UP

People who experience an earthquake describe it in many ways. Some relate a shaking motion while others say that the ground seemed to "roll" beneath their feet.
How did people describe this earthquake?

_____

_____

_____

Has anyone in your class ever lived through an earthquake? How do they describe it?

_____

_____

_____

_____

_____

_____

_____

_____

_____

SYNONYMS ARE WORDS THAT MEAN ALMOST THE SAME THING.

Examples: Shout, yell, and holler are synonyms.
Sad, sorrowful, and morose are synonyms.

Use your knowledge of synonyms to describe the _____ Earthquake.
First, list all the synonyms you can think of for the following words. Use a thesaurus, friends, or other resources.

Shake: *Crack:*   *Rumble:*   *Fall:*

_____   _____   _____   _____

_____   _____   _____   _____

_____   _____   _____   _____

NOW, USE YOUR SYNONYMS IN PHRASES LIKE THIS:

Shake like a milkshake
Rumble with the sound of a car without a muffler

Crack the size of the Mississippi River
Fell hard like a sack of potatoes

My phrases:

_____

_____

_____

My best phrase:

_____

_____

_____

Name _____

THE WAVES

Shock waves are the motion people felt during the _____ Earthquake. These waves came in three stages, or kinds of waves:

p-waves, short for primary waves, which are the first to hit
s-waves, short for secondary waves, which are the next to hit
l-waves, short for large waves (also called surface waves), are the last to hit

These waves have different speeds and do different types of damage. See the "Waves That Destroy" handout for more information. All three kinds of waves have the potential to ruin property and lives.

The people in the _____ Earthquake felt all three types of waves. Use the speed of p-, s-, and l-waves to figure out these problems.

> **p-waves: 4 miles per second**
> **s-waves: 2 miles per second**
> **l-waves: 2 miles per second, sometimes slower**

1. Choose a city about 20 miles away from the epicenter
of the _____ Earthquake.
It took _____5_____ seconds (20 miles ÷ 4 miles/sec) for the first p-waves to hit.
It took _____ seconds for the s-waves to hit.
It took _____ seconds for the l-waves to hit.

2. The city the earthquake was named for was
_____ miles from the actual epicenter of the earthquake. That means:

It took _____ seconds for the p-waves to hit.
It took _____ seconds for the s-waves to hit.
It took _____ seconds for the l-waves to hit.

3. If you were standing on a spot that was 17 miles from the epicenter of _____ Earthquake, it would have taken _____ seconds for the first p-waves to hit, _____ seconds for the s-waves to hit, and _____ seconds for the l-waves to hit.

Show your work:

THE SAN FRANCISCO EARTHQUAKE

Name _____

Use your "Earthquake Data Sheet" and the "Earthquakes in History" handout to answer the following questions:

1. The San Francisco Earthquake took place in

_____.
　　(year)

The _____ Earthquake took place in

_____.
　　(year)

There were _____ years between this earthquake and the San Francisco Earthquake.

2. The San Francisco Earthquake measured _____ on the Richter Scale.

The _____ Earthquake measured _____ on the Richter Scale.

That is a _____ point difference.

3. The death toll for the San Francisco Earthquake was _____ people.

The death toll for the _____ Earthquake was _____ people.

Why do you think the number of deaths are different?

_____

_____

_____

_____

_____

4. Read about the San Francisco Earthquake. List two observations people made at the time of the San Francisco Earthquake. What did they see, hear, and feel?

A. _____

_____

B. _____

_____

5. List two observations people made about the _____ Earthquake. What did they do during the quake? How do they feel now that the quake is over? Will they remain in their same homes?

A. _____

_____

B. _____

_____

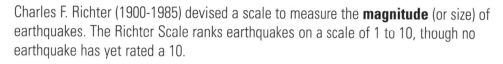

Name _____

THE RICHTER SCALE

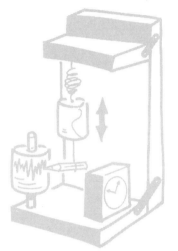

Charles F. Richter (1900-1985) devised a scale to measure the **magnitude** (or size) of earthquakes. The Richter Scale ranks earthquakes on a scale of 1 to 10, though no earthquake has yet rated a 10.

As the numbers on the Richter Scale increase, so does the magnitude of the earthquake. Each number on the Richter Scale stands for 30 times the magnitude of the number just before it. An earthquake that is rated a "4" is 30 times greater than a "3", but a "5" is 900 (30 x 30) greater than a "3". You multiply by 30 each time you go one number higher on the Richter Scale.

Try another one: An earthquake is rated a "6". An aftershock is rated a "3". The magnitude of the "6" is how many times greater than the "3"?

0   1   2   3 ⟶ 4 ⟶ 5 ⟶ 6   7   8   9   10

"6" is three greater than "3" on the Richter Scale; multiply by 30 for each number: 30 x 30 x 30 = **2,700**. A "6" earthquake is 2,700 times greater than a "3" earthquake!

Look at the Earthquakes in History handout. Use the table's information to solve the following problems:

1. The 1992 earthquake in California rated 7.4 on the Richter Scale. The 1964 earthquake in Alaska rated 8.4. Which earthquake was stronger? _____ How much stronger? _____ times stronger.

2. Find an earthquake that is 30 times stronger than another earthquake.

The _____ Earthquake in _____
(year)   (location)

rated _____ was 30 times stronger than the

_____ Earthquake in _____
(year)   (location)
rated _____.

3. The 1976 earthquake in China was how many times stronger that the 1972 earthquake in Nicaragua? _____ times stronger. Show your work:

4. What do you notice about the number of deaths for both earthquakes in the table with a 7.4 rating? Why do you think this is so?

_____

_____

5. The Richter Scale rating for the recent _____ Earthquake was _____. List four earthquakes that were stronger than this earthquake, and four that were weaker.

Stronger		Weaker	
Date	**Location**	**Date**	**Location**
1. _____ _____		1. _____ _____	
2. _____ _____		2. _____ _____	
3. _____ _____		3. _____ _____	
4. _____ _____		4. _____ _____	
5. _____ _____		5. _____ _____	

Name _____

EXPONENTS AND THE RICHTER SCALE

The **exponent** above a number tells you to multiply that number by itself a bunch of times. How many times? Look at the exponent! If the exponent is 2, multiply the number by itself two times. If the exponent is 4, multiply the number by itself four times.

Examples:

$$4^2 = 4 \times 4 = 16$$
$$4^4 = 4 \times 4 \times 4 \times 4 = 256$$
$$3^3 = 3 \times 3 \times 3 = 27$$
$$3^2 = 3 \times 3 = 9$$

How does knowledge of exponents help you understand earthquakes?

Richter Scale magnitudes can be calculated using exponents. If a Richter Scale reading is 2 larger than another quake, it is 30^2 ($30 \times 30 = 900$) times the magnitude. A Richter Scale "7" is 30^5 ($30 \times 30 \times 30 \times 30 \times 30 = 24,300,000$) times more powerful than a "2".

Try these problems:

1. The recent _____ Earthquake rated a _____ on the Richter Scale. That is 30 times greater than which quake listed on the Earthquake History handout? (Choose the quake closest to the Richter Scale rating you need.)

Answer: _____

2. The recent _____ Earthquake rated a _____ on the Richter Scale. That is 30^2 times less than which quake listed on the Earthquakes in History handout? (Choose the quake closest to the Richter Scale reading you need.)

Answer: _____

3. Which quake on the Earthquake History handout was 30^2 (or 900) times greater that another quake?

_____ was 30^2 greater than _____

4. Which quake was 30^1 greater than another quake?

_____ was 30^1 greater than _____

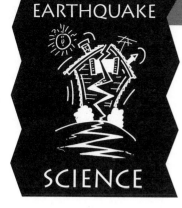

Name _____

THE MODIFIED MERCALLI SCALE

Giuseppe Mercalli (1850 -1914), devised the **Modified Mercalli Intensity Scale** to describe how earthquakes feel to people. The Mercalli Scale also describes what earthquakes do to buildings and people.

List two statements of people who lived through the _____ Earthquake.

A. _____

B. _____

List two ways that this earthquake damaged buildings and property.

C. _____

D. _____

Look at the Modified Mercalli Scale below.

THE MODIFIED MERCALLI SCALE

Scale	Intensity Felt
I	Only instruments feel the ground shaking.
II	People standing still feel some movement.
III	Hanging objects swing and the ground moves.
IV	Walls creak and dishes rattle.
V	Doors swing open; water sloshes from glasses.
VI	Walking is difficult; pictures fall off walls.
VII	Standing is hard; bricks break off buildings.
VIII	Chimneys tumble; driving a car is difficult.
IX	Pipes burst and foundations crack.
X	Landslides occur; brick homes are destroyed.
XI	Railroad tracks bend and the ground cracks open.
XII	Most buildings are destroyed; some rivers divert.

An earthquake will have many different Mercalli ratings, depending on how far the observer is from the earthquake's epicenter. Give a Mercalli rating to each of the observations made during the quake.

Mercalli Rating	Reason
A. _____	_____
B. _____	_____
C. _____	_____
D. _____	_____

Name _____

HAIKU: EXPRESS YOURSELF

People who survive an earthquake often need the help of counselors to understand their experiences. Perhaps they have lost their homes, possessions, or loved ones. Maybe they live in fear of another earthquake and find it hard to get through the day.

Sometimes counselors use writing or drawing activities to help children cope with their feelings. Did survivors of the _____ Earthquake write or draw about their experiences? Look in your school or city library to find personal accounts of earthquakes.

Write a haiku about the _____ Earthquake. A **haiku** is an unrhymed Japanese poem that has three lines. Each line has a certain number of syllables:

first line:	**5 syllables**
second line:	**7 syllables**
third line:	**5 syllables**

1. First make a list of words that describe the _____ Earthquake. Here are a few to start you off:

RUMBLING   _____

DESTRUCTION   _____

SHAKING   _____

SAFETY   _____

SHOCK   _____

2. Write a few phrases here:

RUMBLING COMING CLOSER AND CLOSER

_____

_____

_____

_____

3. Now try to make some of the phrases 5 or 7 syllables long.

_____

_____

_____

_____

_____

_____

WRITE YOUR FINISHED HAIKU BELOW:

Title: _____

first line: _____

second line: _____

third line: _____

Name _____

CONTINENTAL DRIFTERS

This earth's crust is made up of thirteen different **continental plates.** These plates move and drift up to two inches per year.

The _____ Earthquake was the result of two plates scraping against each other, bumping into each other, or pulling apart from each other.

The movement of the plates is called **continental drift.** A German meteorologist named Alfred Wegner wrote the theory of continental drift in 1912. He theorized that the continents were connected in one big piece millions of years ago, but then broke apart and drifted.

You can see how this drifting, scraping, bumping and separating works. Try this:

1. Make a photocopy of the map below. Mark the _____ Earthquake on the map.

2. Cut along the shorelines of the seven continents. Leave Europe and Asia as one big piece: Eurasia.

3. Arrange the pieces on your desk as they were before you cut them out. Look at a world map if you forgot.

4. Now, push the continents together until they are one solid land mass.

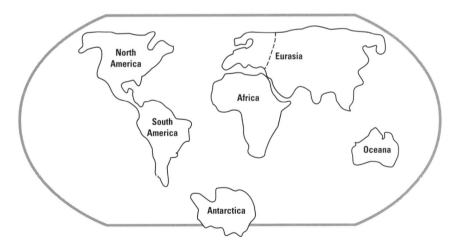

Did the edges fit perfectly? _____
What happened to the extra pieces?

What happened to the missing pieces?

_____

_____

_____

_____

EARTHQUAKE
MATH

Name _____

RING OF FIRE

Earthquakes tend to happen most often along the edges of the the plates that surround the Pacific Ocean. These plates are scraping, bumping, and separating, causing earthquakes as well as volcanic eruptions. Because so many earthquakes and volcanic eruptions happen here, this area is called the **Ring of Fire.**

Use the map below to plot the location of the _____ Earthquake. Also plot the earthquakes listed on the "Earthquake History" handout.

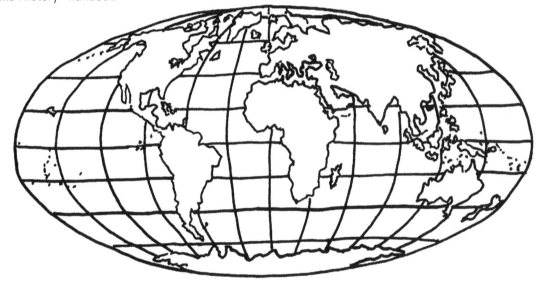

1. How many earthquakes did you plot? _____

2. How many earthquakes were not located in the Ring of Fire? _____

3. How many earthquakes were located in the Ring of Fire? _____

4. Show these numbers as fractions:

Number of earthquakes not in the Ring of Fire = _____
Number of total earthquakes

Number of earthquakes in the Ring of Fire = _____
Number of total earthquakes

5. Which fraction is greater?_____

MATH

Name _____

TRIANGULATION

The **epicenter** of an earthquake is the point on the Earth's surface directly above the plates that scraped, bumped, or separated. Where was the epicenter of the _____ Earthquake? _____

Seismologists can identify the epicenter of an earthquake using a process called **triangulation.** You will see why this process is called triangulation when you do the exercise below.

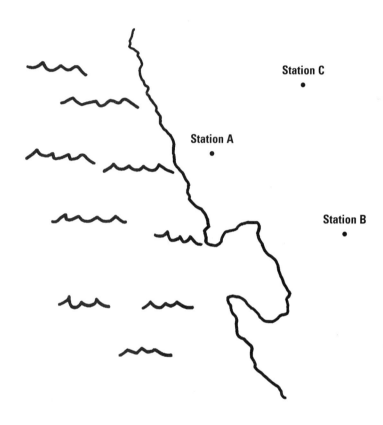

Station C

Station A

Station B

YOU WILL NEED:

- **compass**
- **centimeter ruler**

DIRECTIONS:

1. Using the map below, locate the epicenter of an imaginary earthquake. Seismologists at Quake Stations A, B, and C determined they were the following distances away from the epicenter.

    Quake Station A: 40 kilometers
    Quake Station B: 35 kilometers
    Quake Station C: 60 kilometers

2. Using a compass and the scale shown (1 cm = 10 kilometers), draw a circle centered at Station A with a 4-cm radius.

3. Draw the circles for Stations B and C.

    The radius for Station B, 35 kilometers is _____ cm.
    The radius for Station C, 60 kilometers is _____ cm.

The point where all three circles intersect is the epicenter.

4. Finding the epicenter of an earthquake is called triangulation because:

_____

_____

_____

© Learning Resources, Inc.

EARTHQUAKE

ART

Name _____

EARTHQUAKE SAFETY TIPS

Your chances of surviving an earthquake are greatly improved if you follow basic earthquake safety procedures. How did the survivors of the _____ Earthquake follow safety procedures?

_____

_____

_____

You can share your knowledge of earthquake safety with others. Draw one idea you have for a poster on earthquake safety. Check the Safety Rules on the "Earthquakes in History" handout. Add any other ideas you have.

Sketch your poster idea below.

**Sketch another idea for a
safety poster of a safety concern in your school.**

Title: _____

Title: _____

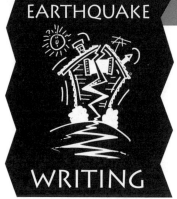

EARTHQUAKE WRITING

Name _____

SEEING THE FUTURE

The first waves of an earthquake, the primary waves, are the first signs of an earthquake… or are they? Measurements are taken regularly along fault lines to see if any movement has occurred. Also, some scientists are researching activities in the Earth's crust that may give us advance warning of an earthquake.

Was the _____ Earthquake predicted by scientists? If so, what did they predict?

_____

_____

Now it is your turn to make some predictions of your own. Try to **hypothesize** (guess) about the future. To increase your chance of being correct, use all the information you can find before you make your predictions.

MY PREDICTIONS

Date I made my predictions: _____

My science grade this term: _____

My favorite activity to do after school by the end of this school year: _____

Where my family will go on our next vacation:

_____

Will one of my classmates break one of his/her bones and need to wear a cast this year? _____

If so, who? _____

What gift will I receive for my birthday next year? (If you don't celebrate birthdays, predict what you will give to someone else.) _____

My height by the end of the school year: _____

How I will be wearing my hair at the end of the school year: _____

Save this sheet and the sheets of your classmates in a folder to be opened at the end of the school year!

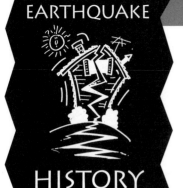

EARTHQUAKES IN HISTORY

DATE	LOCATION	RICHTER SCALE	DEATHS
January 26, 1531	Lisbon, Portugal	?	30,000
January 23, 1556	Shensi, China	?	830,000
October 11, 1737	Calcutta, India	?	300,000
August 31, 1886	Charleston, South Carolina, USA	?	60
June 15, 1896	Riku-Ugo, Japan	?	22,000
June 12, 1897	Assam, India	8.7	1,500
April 18, 1906	San Francisco, California, USA	8.3	503
December 16, 1920	Kansu, China	8.6	160,000
December 26, 1932	Kansu, China	7.6	70,000
January 24, 1939	Chillan, Chile	8.3	28,000
December 27, 1939	Erzincan, Turkey	8.0	23,000
February 29, 1960	Agadir, Morocco	5.9	14,000
March 27, 1964	Alaska, USA	8.4	131
March 28, 1970	Western Turkey	7.4	1,086
December 23, 1972	Managua, Nicaragua	6.2	5,000
July 28, 1976	Tangshan, China	8.2	242,000
November 23, 1977	Northern Argentina	8.2	100
November 23, 1980	Southern Italy	7.2	3,800
September 19, 1985	Michoacan, Mexico	7.9	9,500
July 16, 1990	Luzon, Phillipines	7.7	1,621
June 28, 1992	Yucca Valley, California, USA	7.4	1

EARTHQUAKE SAFETY RULES

1. During a quake, STAY PUT! If you are inside, do not try to get out until the shaking is over. If you are outside, do not run inside.
2. If you are in a classroom, get under a heavy table or desk.
3. If you are at home, stand under a doorway.
4. After the quake, shut off any gas or water lines that might be damaged to prevent fire or flooding.
5. If you are near a beach or coast, move to higher ground immediately. A tsunami could be on its way!

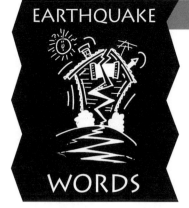

EARTHQUAKE WORDS

EARTHQUAKE GLOSSARY

continental drift – the slow movement of the plates that make up the Earth's crust

epicenter – the point on the Earth's surface directly above an earthquake's hypocenter

exponent – the number above and to the right of a number that tells you how many times to multiply that number by itself

hypocenter – the point under the Earth's surface where an earthquake begins

l-wave (large wave) – the final waves felt during an earthquake

magnitude – the size of the energy released in an earthquake

Modified Mercalli Scale – a scale that describes how strong an earthquake feels to people

plates – the thirteen "pieces" that make up the Earth's crust

p-wave (primary wave) – the first waves felt during an earthquake

Richter Scale – a scale used to rate the energy released by an earthquake

Ring of Fire – the location of many of the Earth's active volcanoes and earthquakes; the Ring of Fire encircles the Pacific Ocean

seismologist – a scientist who studies earthquakes

s-wave (secondary wave) – the second and most powerful waves felt during an earthquake

triangulation – a way to find the epicenter of an earthquake using three different measurements

CHILDREN'S LITERATURE ON EARTHQUAKES

- **Aylesworth, Thomas G. *Geological Disasters.* New York: Franklin Watts, 1979.**
  In this informative book, children will look at recent disasters as examples to learn the relationship between earthquakes and volcanoes, what causes them, and what can be done, if anything, to predict them.

- **Bethancourt, T. Ernesto. *The Tomorrow Connection.* New York: Holiday House, 1984.**
  Richie Gilroy and Matty Owen travel back in time to 1906, where they join Harry Houdini on the vaudeville circuit. Their travels land them in San Francisco just before the great earthquake, looking for the doorway to the present.

- **Buck, Pearl S. *The Big Wave.* New York: Harper Collins Publishers, 1947.**
  When a "big wave" wipes out Jiya's home and fishing village in Japan, Jiya struggles to recover, and learns to appreciate the beauty of life.

- **Holden, Martin & Karen Holden. *Natural Disasters: Unleashing the Fury of Nature.* New York: Michael Friedman Publishing Group, Inc., 1990.**
  In this impressive picture book, graphic color photos and descriptive text show the tremendous force of natural disasters, including earthquakes, volcanoes, tropical hurricanes, tornadoes, and el niño.

- **Kudlinski, Kathleen. *Earthquake!* New York: Viking Press, 1993.**
  In the wake of the San Francisco earthquake and fire, Philip must rescue his family's horses.

- **Lewis, Thomas P. *Hill of Fire.* New York: Harper & Row, 1971.**
  Pablo and his father discover a "hill of fire" growing in their cornfield. Beginning readers will delight in this true story of Paricutin, the volcano that erupted in Mexico in 1943.

- **Paananen, Eloise. *Tremor!* New York: Julian Messner, 1982.**
  This informative book satisfies older children's curiosity about earthquakes, with historical accounts and text about what causes them, their relationship to volcanoes, how to measure and predict them, and what to do before, during and after a tremor.

- **Place, Marian T. *Mount St. Helens.* New York: Dodd, Mead & Company, 1981.**
  Readers can share eyewitness and survivor accounts that tell the story of Washington state's Mount St. Helens volcano which erupted unexpectedly on May 18, 1980; includes graphic black-and-white photographs.

- **Stein, R. Conrad. *The San Francisco Earthquake.* Chicago: Childrens Press, 1983.**
  This nonfiction account of the San Francisco Earthquake helps readers understand how lives are affected by such a great catastrophe.

- **VanCleave, Janice. *Earthquakes.* New York: John Wiley & Sons, Inc., 1993.**
  This collection of 20 science projects and experiments brings new perspective to the study of earthquakes. Children benefit from hands-on exploration to answer probing questions like "How do earthquakes crack the Earth's surface?" and "How do earthquakes affect unbraced frame structures?"

- **Verne, Jules. *Journey to the Center of the Earth.* New York: Viking Penguin, 1965.**
  Join a daring expedition in this thrilling adventure tale about a group of explorers who travel deep beneath the Earth's surface to find what lies at its core.

- **Wright, Glen. *A Mountain Blows Its Top.* Provo, Utah: ARO Publishing Inc., 1981.**
  Fascinating true stories and authentic photos of volcanoes, earthquakes and avalanches give testimony to the theory that the Earth's surface is ever-changing.

TEACHING NOTES
Tornadoes

The Tornadoes Unit is designed to be ready to go! When a tornado happens, reproduce enough copies for your entire class, and do the activities together. Most activity sheets ask students first to fill in the name of the tornado you are studying.

Here are some suggestions to make the most of your curriculum:

- Have students bring in newspaper or magazine articles on the tornado you are studying to share them with the rest of the class.

- Collect periodical clippings, an atlas, a globe, maps, library books, and the projects your students complete in one area of your classroom. Call it the **Tornado Information Center.**

- The activity pages are arranged in an order that seems to "flow" well. However, feel free to use the pages in a different order depending on your curricular needs.

- The table below outlines each activity with a general curricular area and the topics covered. Some activities cover topics from more than one curricular area.

STUDENT ACTIVITY CURRICULAR AREA	TOPICS	PAGE
KWL	Language Arts	general knowledge, written expression	27
Gloom and Doom	Art	artistic expression, colors	28
Getting Closer	Math	speed, division	29
Make a Model of a Tornado	Science	modeling, observation	30
On the Beaten Path	Social Studies	map reading, scaling	31
How Windy Was It?	Science	measurement, observation	32
That's Intense!	Math	classification, data analysis	33
Blown Away	Language Arts	5 W's and H, written expression	34
Windy Pressure	Science	observation, comparison	35
Tornadoes Happen	Math	bar graphs, pie graphs	36
Tornado Alley	Social Studies	map reading	37
I Heard That	Language Arts	similes, written expression	38
Who Did What?	Math	logic	39
Staying Safe	Language Arts	safety, maps, written expression	40
Survive, Stay Alive	Social Studies	safety, artistic expression	41

Selected answers:

page 29: 1. 3 miles **2.** 2.4 miles **3.** 20 seconds **4.** Light is faster than sound **5.** Sound = 740 mph, Light = 186,000 miles per second

page 33. 1. 6 **2.** It depends **3.** 32, 39, 44, 48, 62, 48

page 36: May, June, Apr., July, Aug., Mar., Sep., Nov., Oct., Feb., Dec., Jan.

page 39: Juan = Red Cross, Kim = Police, Olga = National Guard, Ben = Paramedic

Name _____

TORNADO DATA SHEET

LOCATION:

Record anything you know about the town or city suffering the most damage below:

1. _____
   _____
2. _____
   _____
3. _____
   _____
4. _____
   _____
5. _____
   _____
6. _____
   _____

Most tornadoes are given the name of the city or town that suffered the most damage. The tornado you are studying has been named the _____ Tornado.

Date of tornado: _____

Were there several tornadoes? _____ If so, how many? _____

What was the average wind speed? _____

DAMAGE:

How many people were killed?

_____

How many people were left homeless?

_____

How many homes were destroyed?

_____

What is the estimate of the cost of the damage?

_____

WEATHER INFORMATION:

Record anything you learned about the weather conditions at the time of the storm below:

1. _____
2. _____
3. _____
4. _____

ADDITIONAL INFORMATION:

Record any additional information or observations in the space to the right. Use the back of this sheet if necessary.

_____
_____
_____
_____

Name _____

KWL

KWL

K —What I already <u>K</u>now   **W** — What I <u>W</u>ant to know

L — What I have <u>L</u>earned

KWL is a tool that scientists use to investigate. You can do a KWL as you investigate this tornado.

First, write down everything you already know about this tornado. Where and when did it happen? Was it one twister, or more? What kind of damage did it cause, and what happened to the people near it? Don't worry if you are right or wrong. You will be checking your facts later.

WHAT I ALREADY KNOW:

1. _____

2. _____

3. _____

4. _____

5. _____

6. _____

7. _____

Now, write down anything you want to know about this tornado. What questions do you have about this tornado? What exactly is a tornado? What was the location like before the tornado? How many buildings were damaged? How long did it last? Write down any questions that come to mind.

WHAT I WANT TO KNOW:

1. _____

2. _____

3. _____

4. _____

5. _____

6. _____

7. _____

WHAT I HAVE LEARNED:

As you learn more about this tornado, you will complete the "L" part of the KWL. "L" stands for what you have learned. When you learn something new or answer one of your questions, write it down on the back of this sheet.

Name _____

GLOOM AND DOOM

Though a tornado can begin as an ordinary thunderstorm, often there are clues that something stronger than a rainstorm is building. The color of the sky is one of the clues that a tornado may be coming.

Have you ever seen a thunderstorm which spawned a tornado? If so, you may have noticed the sky turning a greenish, purplish color. Others have described the color as yellow to brown. Scientists believe this color is the reflection of the ground's color against the low-hanging clouds.

Look for a description of the color of the _____ Tornado's sky in the newspaper. Draw a scene of the sky before the _____ Tornado, as you imagine it, in the space below.

YOU WILL NEED:

• **colored chalk**
• **colored pencils**
• **colored markers**

DIRECTIONS:

1. Colored chalk works best because it is easiest to blend the colors. Apply one color at a time.

2. Use the flat part of your first three fingertips to blend the colors on the paper. Rub with your fingertips in a circular motion until your color has a soft, fluffy look.

3. Whatever materials you choose, start with the light colors first. You always can add color layers to make it darker.

4. If your shade becomes too dark, apply a layer of white, yellow, or gray to make it lighter.

Name _____

GETTING CLOSER

Inside the funnel cloud of the _____ Tornado, there was almost constant lightning. Where there is lightning, there is thunder.

In any thunderstorm or tornado, it is possible to tell when the storm is getting closer. You can do this by watching for the lightning, and listening for the thunder.

If you had been near the _____ Tornado (but in a safe place!), you could have used this method to tell how many miles away the storm was. You can use the following method any time there is a thunderstorm.

YOU WILL NEED:

• **a clock or stopwatch with a second hand**
• **a thunderstorm!**

DIRECTIONS:

1. Watch for a flash of lightning.
2. Using a clock or stopwatch, count the number of seconds between the flash of lightning and the first sound of thunder.
3. Divide the number of seconds by 5. The answer tells you how many miles away the lightning struck.

TRY THESE PROBLEMS.

Show your work below each problem.

1. Lightning flashes. 15 seconds later, thunder is heard. The lightning struck _____ miles away.

2. Lightning flashes. 12 seconds later, thunder is heard. The lightning struck _____ miles away.

3. Lightning strikes 4 miles away. The thunder will be heard _____ seconds later.

4. What does this experiment tell you about the speed of light versus the speed of sound?

_____

_____

_____

5. Look up the speed of both light and sound in a science book.

Sound _____

Light _____

© Learning Resources, Inc.

MAKE A MODEL OF A TORNADO

Name _____

Try building your own mini tornado in a bottle!

YOU WILL NEED:

- **two empty plastic 2-liter bottles**
- **a plastic or metal washer**
- **masking tape**
- **food coloring**
- **water**

DIRECTIONS:

1. Fill one 2-liter bottle half-full with water. Add food coloring until the water is a color you like.

2. Put a plastic washer over the top opening of the bottle.

3. Take the cap off another empty 2-liter bottle. Turn it upside down, on top of the other bottle.

4. Wrap masking tape around the two necks so the bottles are attached. Make sure the tape is tight so the water inside will not leak out.

5. Flip the bottles over so the full bottle is on top. Now, gently swirl the bottles around to start the water spinning.

6. Watch the water swirl down from the top bottle to the bottom bottle. Draw a picture of what you see.

7. Try this three times in a row and time it. How long does it take the water to go from top to bottom?

    Trial 1 _____

    Trial 2 _____

    Trial 3 _____

8. Calculate the average time for a trial.

    Trial average _____

WHAT I SAW:

Name _____

ON THE BEATEN PATH

The _____ Tornado occurred at

_____ on _____,

(time)   (day of week)

_____.

(date)

It lasted for _____ minutes and touched down on the ground _____ times.

Read the following sources and make your own map showing the path of the _____ Tornado in the space below.

- **TV**
- **Cable TV**
- **Newspapers**
- **Other people**
- **Maps of the area**

Include in your map:

1. The surrounding area: land, rivers, mountains, roads, etc.

2. A key to what all the symbols mean.

3. A scale telling how many miles (or kilometers) are equal to one centimeter.

4. A large funnel symbol to show where the tornado first touched down.

5. A dotted line in a bold color, such as red, showing the path of the _____ Tornado. Add small arrows along the dotted line to show which direction the tornado was moving.

6. Small funnel symbols along the dotted line to show any other places that the tornado touched down.

7. One last large funnel symbol to show the end of the tornado's path.

SCIENCE

Name _____

HOW WINDY WAS IT?

The powerful winds of a tornado can reach speeds of up to 350 mph! What were the wind speeds of the _____ Tornado? _____
What was the top speed? _____

You can make an instrument to measure wind speed, called an **anemometer.**

YOU WILL NEED:

- **ping pong ball**
- **tape**
- **protractor**
- **string**

DIRECTIONS:

1. Cut a piece of string that is 12 inches (30 cm) long. Tape one end to a ping pong ball.

2. Tape the other end of the string to a protractor as shown.

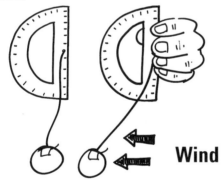

Wind

3. Go outside with your anemometer. Face the wind. Guess how fast the wind is blowing. _____ mph

4. Hold the protractor with the base perpendicular to the ground, facing the wind. The wind will blow the ping pong ball so the string slides across the protractor. Record the number marked by the string. The number will be between 0 and 90 degrees.

5. Repeat the test three times and record the degree readings below.

   Trial 1 _____

   Trial 2 _____

   Trial 3 _____

6. Use this chart to match up your degrees with the wind speed.

Degrees	Speed (mph)
0	0
5	7
10	9
15	10
20	12
25	13
30	15
35	16
40	18
45	20
50	21
55	23
60	26
65	29
70	33
75	38

7. Keep track of the wind speed for one week.

8. What was the average wind speed for this week? _____ mph

Name _____

THAT'S INTENSE!

List some of the damage caused by the
_____ Tornado. Try to be
as specific as possible when you describe the
damage. How tall were the trees that were blown
over? Were roofs torn off or just their shingles?
Were cars turned over, tossed around, or lifted
up and put down again hundreds of feet away?

A. _____

_____

B. _____

_____

C. _____

_____

Dr. T. Theodore Fujita (pronounced "few-GEE-ta") and Allan Pearson devised
a scale that ranks tornadoes by their intensity (or strength). The greater the
wind speed, the higher the Fujita/Pearson Number. Tornadoes with high
ratings on the Fujita/Pearson Tornado Intensity Scale cause greater damage
than tornadoes with lower ratings.

Fujita Number	Wind Speed (mph)	Damage	Examples
F0	40-72	Light	Broken branches, some windows shattered
F1	73-112	Moderate	Tree trunks snapped, shingles torn off roofs
F2	113-157	Strong	Trees uprooted, roofs torn off
F3	158-206	Severe	Walls blown down, cars turned over
F4	207-269	Devastating	Homes leveled, cars tossed around
F5	270-318	Incredible	Homes blown away, cars thrown 300 ft. or more

Answer the following questions:

1. How many Fujita Numbers are possible? _____

2. How many miles per hour (mph) must the wind speed
increase before a tornado receives the next higher
Fujita Number? _____

3. What is the range of wind speeds for each Fujita
Number? (The first one is done: 72 – 40 = 32)

_____32_____ mph for F0

_____ mph for F1

_____ mph for F2

_____ mph for F3

_____ mph for F4

_____ mph for F5.

Show your work.

4. According to this list, the _____ Tornado
would be given a Fujita/Pearson Number of _____.

TORNADO

WRITING

BLOWN AWAY

Name _____

In the movie *The Wizard of Oz,* a twister (tornado) transported Dorothy to the Land of Oz. She took one look around and knew she "wasn't in Kansas anymore."

During severe tornadoes, with wind speeds of 270-318 mph, homes can be blown away, but rarely in one piece. Cars can be picked up and put down again hundreds of feet away.

1. In the _____ Tornado, were any homes or cars moved? _____
What other objects did you read about that were transported by the tornado's strong winds?

_____

_____

_____

_____

_____

2. Write a realistic description telling where the _____ Tornado transported you and your belongings. Take into account the actual wind speed of the _____ Tornado.

Include in your paragraph:
- <u>Who</u> or <u>What</u> was blown away.
- <u>When</u> it happened.
- <u>Where</u> it happened, and where you landed.
- <u>Why</u> this happened.
- <u>How</u> this happened.

_____

_____

_____

_____

_____

_____

_____

_____

_____

_____

_____

_____

_____

_____

3. Now, turn this sheet over, and write another paragraph that is fantasy. You can be transported wherever you choose. Let your imagination run wild!

Name _____

WINDY PRESSURE

What was the highest recorded wind speed in the _____ Tornado? _____ mph. The faster the wind blew in the _____ Tornado, the lower the air pressure became. This drop in air pressure that accompanies an increase in wind speed was discovered by Daniel Bernoulli (pronounced ber-NOO-lee) in 1738.

Try the following experiment to show how objects are affected by lowered air pressure.

YOU WILL NEED:

- **2 ping pong or small Styrofoam balls**
- **tape**
- **thread**
- **pencil**
- **scissors**

DIRECTIONS:

1. Cut two 6-inch (15-cm) pieces of thread.
2. Tape one piece of thread to a ping pong ball, and the other piece to another ball.
3. Tie the two loose ends to a pencil like this:

Make sure there is about 2 inches (5 cm) between the ping pong balls, and that the balls are side by side.

4. Blow air between the two ping pong balls.
5. Blow air past the ball on the left.

6. Draw what happened below.

Blowing air between the balls.

[ ]

Blowing air to the left of the balls.

[ ]

7. When you blew between the two balls, the air pressure _____ between the balls.
   (increased/decreased)

8. When you blew to the left of the two balls, the air pressure _____ between the balls.
   (increased/decreased)

MATH

TORNADOES HAPPEN

Name _____

Look at the bar graph below to see the average number of tornadoes sighted in the United States during one year.

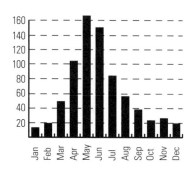

What month did the _____ Tornado occur?

_____

Is this a month that usually has a lot of tornadoes?

_____

Using the graph above, list the months of the year in the order of tornado frequency. Start with the month that has the *most* tornadoes, and end your list with the month that has the *least* tornadoes. Circle those months that have the same number of tornadoes.

1. _____   7. _____

2. _____   8. _____

3. _____   9. _____

4. _____   10. _____

5. _____   11. _____

6. _____   12. _____

Use the circle below to create a pie graph of tornado frequency.

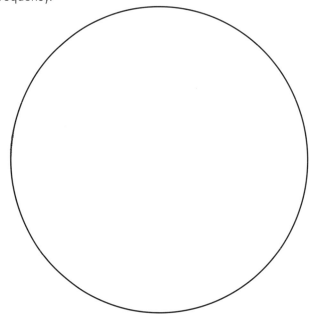

1. Divide the circle into 16 equal sections, each standing for 50 tornadoes.

2. Color a piece of the pie for each month that equals the number of tornadoes that happen in that month. For example, for April you would color two pieces of pie for 100 tornadoes, plus a little piece for 5 more tornadoes, for a total of about 105 tornadoes.

3. Label each month's "pie piece."

4. Put a star in the piece of the pie when the _____ Tornado happened.

TORNADO
GEOGRAPHY

Name _____

TORNADO ALLEY

The _____ Tornado occurred in which state? _____ Does this state have many tornadoes, or is it one of the luckier states that has few or no tornadoes each year?

Tornadoes travel easiest across flat, open land. Look at a topographical map of the United States, and guess which eight states have the most tornadoes each year.

1. Use an atlas to locate the following states: Arkansas, Illinois, Indiana, Iowa, Kansas, Missouri, Oklahoma, and Texas.

2. Color each state on the map above. Why do you think these states are named "Tornado Alley"?

_____

_____

3. Show with a funnel cloud symbol where the _____ Tornado happened.

4. Add the capital of each state in Tornado Alley. Put a star symbol where each capital city is located, and write the city's name.

I HEARD THAT...

Name _____

Inside a tornado, there is almost constant lightning. This lightning produces lots of thunder. If you were near a tornado, you might need to plug your ears!

People have described the sound of tornadoes in many different ways. Read the newspaper or watch television, and list three ways people have described the sound of the _____ Tornado.

1._____

2._____

3._____

Here are some ways people have described the sound of a tornado:

– like a runaway freight train
– like a swarming hive of bees
– like a jet engine

A **simile** is a descriptive phrase that uses the words "like" or "as." For example:

– pretty as a picture   *– swim like a fish*
– cuts like a knife   *– big as the ocean*
– cool as a cucumber   *– hungry like a wolf*

Were any similes used to describe the _____ Tornado? If so, write them below:

_____

_____

_____

Now, write four similes about the _____ Tornado. Use similes to describe the look, power, danger, effect, or result of the tornado.

1._____

2._____

3._____

4._____

TORNADO

LOGIC

Name _____

WHO DID WHAT?

The rescue workers after the _____ Tornado each had important jobs. Working together, they helped victims of the disaster in many different ways. Investigate the roles that the Red Cross, National Guard, local police, and paramedics played in this disaster.

Read the clues below to find out which job belongs to which type of rescue worker in an imaginary disaster. The chart below will help you keep track of the information. Put an "**✗**" to show a definite "NO" and a **✔** to show a definite "YES."

	Juan	**Kim**	**Olga**	**Ben**
Police				
Red Cross				
Paramedic				
National Guard				

You may need to read the following clues more than once.

1. Ben gave medical attention to survivors.

2. Juan is a teacher, but he is called upon in natural disasters.

3. Kim is not a volunteer.

4. The governor calls on Olga to preserve order in an emergency.

When you think that you have solved the puzzle, write the occupation of each worker next to his/her name.

Juan _____

Kim _____

Olga _____

Ben _____

Name _____

STAYING SAFE

1. Is your school located in an area that has tornadoes ? _____

2. Is your school located in an area that has hurricanes? _____

3. Is your school located in an area that has earthquakes? _____

4. List any natural disasters that you know of that have happened near your school. Ask adults what they remember.

A. _____

B. _____

C. _____

All schools must have a plan in case of a natural disaster. This plan includes a map of how each class will reach a safe place.

Ask your school staff for their disaster plan. If the plan includes a map, draw the part of the map that shows where your class is supposed to go in case of a disaster. If the plan does not include a map, draw one below after reading the plan's description of where your class is supposed to go.

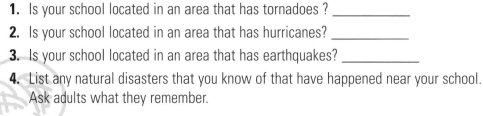

ROOM _____ DISASTER PLAN

Directions to a safe place: _____

_____

_____

TORNADO

SAFETY

Name _____

SURVIVE, STAY ALIVE

Your chances of surviving a tornado are greatly improved if you follow a few basic tornado safety rules.

Did the survivors of the _____ Tornado follow safety rules? _____

How did they stay safe? _____

_____

_____

_____

You can share your knowledge of tornado safety with others. Draw one idea you have for a poster on tornado safety. Check the Tornado Safety Tips on the Tornadoes in History Sheet. Add other ideas you have.

Sketch your poster idea below.

Sketch another idea for a safety poster of a safety concern in your school.

Title:

Title:

_____

_____

© Learning Resources, Inc.

TORNADOES IN HISTORY

DATE	LOCATION	DEATHS
May 7, 1840	Natchez, Mississippi	317
May 27, 1896	St. Louis, Missouri	306
March 18, 1925	Missouri and Illinois	689
November 11, 1925	Belleville, Arkansas	53
April 12, 1927	Rock Springs, Texas	74
March 21, 1932	Alabama	268
April 6, 1936	Gainesville, Georgia	203
September 29, 1938	Charleston, South Carolina	32
April 27, 1942	Rogers County, Oklahoma	52
June 9, 1953	Worcester, Massachusetts	92
May 25, 1955	Udall, Kansas	80
March 3, 1966	Jackson, Mississippi	58
February 21, 1971	Mississippi Delta	181
May 22, 1987	Saratoga, Texas	29
November 16, 1989	Newburgh, New York	9

TORNADO SAFETY TIPS

1. The safest location in your home is in the basement, under a staircase or beneath a sturdy table.
2. If you do not have a basement, go to a central hall, bathroom, or closet. **STAY AWAY FROM WINDOWS!**
3. At school, follow your teacher's directions. Stay out of the gym or auditorium; large roofs can collapse.
4. If you are in a mobile home, get outside and lie face down in a ditch, covering your head with your hands. You are safer outside a mobile home than you are inside.
5. Never try to outrun a storm in a car. You could be blown easily off the road or picked up by the twister.

WATCHES AND WARNINGS

When thunderstorms are in your area, weather forecasters will be watching the skies for the possibility of a tornado. If a weather forecaster issues a **Tornado Watch**, there is a possibility a tornado could develop. You should keep a radio or television turned on to listen for further details. If a **Tornado Warning** is issued, a tornado has been spotted. If it is issued for your area, seek shelter immediately!

TORNADO GLOSSARY

anemometer – an instrument used to measure wind speed

barometer – a device used to measure barometric pressure

barometric pressure – the weight of air above a given location; cold air generally has a higher barometric pressure than warm air

Bernoulli Effect – as air moves faster, its pressure drops

cumulonimbus cloud – a fluffy, tall, rain cloud which produces most tornadoes

disaster plan – the steps you must follow in case of an emergency; you must know these steps and practice them before a disaster occurs

dryline – the line along which cool, dry air meets warm, moist air, and along which many tornadoes form

dust devil – a swirling windstorm, often in the desert; not a tornado

Fujita-Pearson Intensity Scale – a 6-point scale used to rank a tornado by its wind speed

funnel cloud – a tornado that has not yet reached the ground

hail – layered ice balls formed in high-wind thunderstorms

lightning – a large discharge of static electricity around a storm system

lightning rod – a wire used to conduct a bolt of lightning around a structure and to the ground; invented by Benjamin Franklin

thunder – the sound created by expanding air heated by a lightning bolt

tornado – a powerful, whirling storm formed beneath a thunderhead, which funnels warm air upward and cool air downward

Tornado Alley – a region in the central United States where most tornadoes form

Tornado Warning – a warning issued when a tornado has been spotted

Tornado Watch – a weather advisory issued when conditions are ripe for the formation of tornadoes

water spout – a tornado over a body of water

CHILDREN'S LITERATURE ON TORNADOES

- **Berger, Melvin & Gilda. *How's the Weather?* Nashville: Ideals Children's Books, 1993.**
  Bright illustrations, simple text, and easy experiments give children a hands-on introduction to the weather. The book also explores forecasting and why weather often can be difficult to predict.

- **Branley, Franklyn M. *It's Raining Cats and Dogs.* Boston: Houghton Mifflin Company, 1987.**
  This engaging collection of facts, folklore and scientific experiments looks at weather from a different angle. Learn why we have pink or green snow, how to measure the size of raindrops, make a storm in a cakepan, and more.

- **Branley, Franklyn M. *Tornado Alert.* New York: Thomas Y. Crowell, 1988.**
  With a series of dramatic color illustrations, easy-to-read text explains when, where, and how a tornado begins, and what to do in the event of a tornado.

- **Catherall, Ed. *Wind Play.* England: Wayland Publishers, Ltd., 1986.**
  Give children a chance to see for themselves the incredible power of wind. This book of 20 easy experiments is filled with ideas related to weather, including sending wind messages, chasing clouds, gales and storms, and more.

- **De Jong, Meindert. *A Horse Came Running.* New York: Collier Books, 1970.**
  Young Mark is stranded with three injured horses, and must find his way to safety after a twister.

- **George, Jean Craighead. *One Day in the Prairie.* New York: Thomas Y. Crowell, 1986.**
  Animals on a prairie wildlife refuge sense an approaching tornado and seek protection from its threatening winds.

- **Hiscock, Bruce. *The Big Storm.* New York: Atheneum, 1993.**
  Follow the path of the powerful storm that began on March 30, 1982 and crossed the United States for six days following. Beautiful watercolor paintings and illustrations set the tone for this accurate account that explains the weather from both scientific and geographical perspectives.

- **Hopping, Lorraine Jean. *Tornadoes!* New York: Scholastic Inc., 1994.**
  Part of the "Wild Weather" series, this easy reader joins two people as they follow and study tornadoes in the Midwest.

- **Jaroch, Mike. *The Adventures of the Sneeky Sneakers: The Tornado.* Chicago: Childrens Press, 1977.**
  Magical powers from a pair of sneakers help four brothers stop a tornado.

- **Kramer, Stephen. *Tornado.* Minneapolis: Carolrhoda Books, Inc., 1992.**
  Impressive color photographs and easy-to-understand illustrations support a well organized, comprehensive survey of tornadoes, their origins, types, and other facts about this powerful phenomenon.

- **Lambert, David. *The Work of the Wind.* New York: The Bookwright Press, 1984.**
  A moving collection of color photographs and accompanying text shows the impact of all kinds of wind – on land and sea, mountain and desert – with discussion of how man has learned to live with it.

- **Lee, Sally. *Predicting Violent Storms.* New York: Franklin Watts, 1989.**
  Learn the latest techniques for predicting and understanding the weather, including what causes violent storms, forecasting tools, and what goes on at the National Weather Service, plus a chapter on efforts to control the weather.

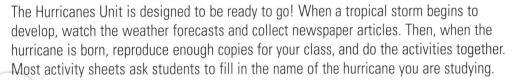

TEACHING NOTES
Hurricanes

The Hurricanes Unit is designed to be ready to go! When a tropical storm begins to develop, watch the weather forecasts and collect newspaper articles. Then, when the hurricane is born, reproduce enough copies for your class, and do the activities together. Most activity sheets ask students to fill in the name of the hurricane you are studying.

Here are some suggestions to make the most of your curriculum:

- Have students bring in newspaper or magazine articles on the tropical storm and hurricane you are studying to share them with the rest of the class.

- Collect periodical clippings, an atlas, a globe, maps, library books, and the projects your students complete in one area of your classroom. Call it the **Hurricane Information Center.**

- The activity pages are arranged in an order that seems to "flow" well. However, feel free to use the pages in a different order depending on your curricular needs.

- The table below outlines each activity with a general curricular area and the topics covered. Some activities cover topics from more than one curricular area.

Selected answers:

page 54: 6. Water level goes up in high pressure, water level goes down in low pressure

page 59: 4. 4 sheets, $78.04

Name _____

HURRICANE DATA SHEET

Follow newspaper reports and record important information on the hurricane as it happens.

Hurricane Name: _____

Date	Longitude	Latitude	Barometric Pressure	Wind Speed

THE BEAUFORT SCALE

Beaufort Number	Wind Speed (mph)	Description	Effect on Objects
0	<1	calm	Smoke rises straight up
1	1-3	light air	Smoke drifts lightly with wind
2	4-7	light breeze	Flags stir, leaves blow
3	8-12	gentle breeze	Flags blow out, leaves blow steadily
4	13-18	moderate breeze	Flags flap, loose paper flies
5	19-24	fresh breeze	Flags ripple, small trees sway
6	25-31	strong breeze	Flags beat, large branches move
7	32-38	moderate gale	Flags extended, whole trees move
8	39-46	fresh gale	Twigs break, walking is hard
9	47-54	strong gale	Houses slightly damaged
10	55-63	whole gale	Trees uprooted, houses damaged
11	64-73	storm	Widespread damage
12	>74	hurricane	Excessive damage

THE SAFFIR-SIMPSON SCALE

The Saffir-Simpson Scale rates wind speeds of hurricane-force winds.

Category	Barometric Pressure	Wind Speed (mph)	Potential Damage
1	> 28.94	74-95	Trees and mobile homes slightly damaged
2	28.50-28.93	96-110	Trees blown over, roofs are lightly damaged
3	27.91-28.49	111-130	Large trees uprooted, mobile homes destroyed
4	27.17-27.90	131-155	Signs blown down, structural damage to buildings
5	< 27.17	> 155	Small buildings destroyed, waters rise 15 feet

Name _____

KWL

KWL

K —What I already <u>K</u>now **W** — What I <u>W</u>ant to know
L — What I have <u>L</u>earned

KWL is a tool that scientists use to investigate. You can do a KWL as you investigate this tornado.

First, write down everything you already know about this hurricane. Where did it happen? What do you know about the places it affected? What was its name? How long did it last? What kind of damage did it cause, and what happened to the people near it? Don't worry if you are right or wrong. You will be checking your facts later.

WHAT I ALREADY KNOW:

1. _____
2. _____
3. _____
4. _____
5. _____
6. _____
7. _____

Now, write down anything you want to know about this hurricane. What questions do you have about this hurricane? What exactly is a hurricane? How did it get its name? How fast did its winds blow? How did it stop? Write down any questions that come to mind.

WHAT I WANT TO KNOW:

1. _____
2. _____
3. _____
4. _____
5. _____
6. _____
7. _____

WHAT I HAVE LEARNED:

As you learn more about this hurricane, you will complete the "L" part of the KWL. "L" stands for what you have learned. When you learn something new or answer one of your questions, write it down on the back of this sheet.

Name _____

A HURRICANE IS BORN

The following rhyme will help you remember when to watch for developing hurricanes:

JUNE, TOO SOON.
JULY, STAND BY.
AUGUST, LOOK OUT!
SEPTEMBER, YOU WILL REMEMBER.
OCTOBER, ALL OVER.

Does the above rhyme fit the time that Hurricane _____ developed? Explain.

_____

_____

_____

Follow the development of Hurricane _____ with your class and teacher. You can watch television for satellite pictures, cable TV (the Weather Channel), or the radio. You also can read about it on the Weather Page of your local newspaper.

Record the development of Hurricane _____ using a timeline.

DIRECTIONS:

1. Draw a straight line down the middle of the back of this sheet to create a timeline.

2. Start at one end of the timeline and mark off the days. Remember, this storm/hurricane could last for several days or even weeks. Keep the same amount of space between each day.

3. Divide each day into A.M. and P. M.

4. Record the following events using labeled dots on your timeline. (Use the Glossary for any terms you do not understand.)
   – Tropical wave develops
   – Tropical disturbance gathers
   – Tropical depression is rotating
   – Tropical storm growing
   – Hurricane is born

5. Include other events on your timeline. You might want to record:
   – damage to property
   – deaths
   – locations of the tropical storm/hurricane as it moves

HURRICANE MATH

Name _____

PLOTTING THE PATH OF A HURRICANE

Latitude and **longitude** are the lines you see on a globe. Latitude lines run parallel to the equator. Latitude lines tell how far north or south a place is from the equator. Longitude lines run from the North Pole to the South Pole; they tell how far east or west a place is from the Prime Meridian, the line running through Greenwich, England.

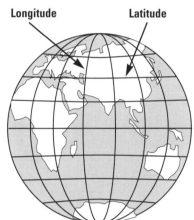

Longitude   Latitude

Here's an easy way to remember the difference between latitude and longitude:

LONGITUDE lines run the long way.
(Notice the word *"long"* in *"long*itude")

LATITUDE lines are like the steps on a ladder.
(Notice that *"latitude"* starts like *"ladder"*)

Watch weather reports and read newspaper articles about Hurricane _____. Hurricane watchers use latitude and longitude to describe where Hurricane _____ is traveling. Record the hurricane's latitude and longitude each day throughout the life of the storm. Write them on the table below.

DATE	TIME	LATITUDE (°, N OR S)	LONGITUDE (°, E OR W)

Make a copy of a map that shows the area where Hurricane _____ traveled, and include longitude and latitude. Plot each of the coordinate pairs above as dots to show where Hurricane _____ was on each day.

Connect the dots to show the path of Hurricane _____.

Name _____

DIFFERENT NAME, SAME HURRICANE

There are different names for large, tropical storms, depending on where they happen. Look up the following terms in your Hurricane Glossary. Fill in the definitions.

HURRICANE: _____

_____

_____

CYCLONE: _____

_____

_____

TYPHOON: _____

_____

_____

Now, label the Earth's four oceans on the map below. Draw three storms on the map: one hurricane, one typhoon, and one cyclone. Label each storm with the name it has been given.

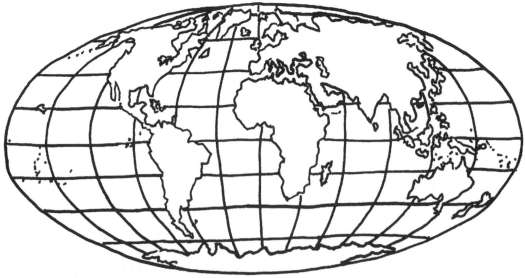

Name _____

NAME THAT HURRICANE

Hurricanes in the Atlantic Ocean are named with male or female names. What was the name of this hurricane? _____ Every six hurricane seasons, the names are used over again. Below is one example of a "Hurricane Year":

Hurricanes Names for 1996
Arthur, Bertha, Cesar, Dolly, Edouard, Fran, Gustav, Hortense, Isidore, Josephine, Klaus, Lili, Marco, Nana, Omar, Paloma, Rene, Sally, Teddy, Vicky, and Wilfred.

Notice that the names alternate from male to female, and that no hurricane names start with the letters Q, U, X, Y or Z. (There are not enough names that begin with those letters.)

Now create a new list of your own using new names.

A _____ H _____ O _____
B _____ I _____ P _____
C _____ J _____ R _____
D _____ K _____ S _____
E _____ L _____ T _____
F _____ M _____ V _____
G _____ N _____ W _____

Try naming the hurricanes after foods. A few hints are included to help you get started.

A ARTICHOKE _____ H _____ O _____
B _____ I _____ P _____
C _____ J JICAMA _____ R _____
D _____ K _____ S _____
E EGGPLANT _____ L _____ T _____
F _____ M _____ V _____
G _____ N _____ W _____

HURRICANE SCIENCE

Name _____

DON'T PRESSURE ME

Look at weather maps of Hurricane _____. Where were the areas of high pressure? _____ Where were the areas of low pressure? _____

When an ocean's water surface temperature is greater than 80 degrees Fahrenheit (26.7° Celcius), a hurricane can form. Evaporating water gathers into an area of low pressure. In general, warm air is low pressure (less dense), and cool air is high pressure (more dense). Warm air expands and the cool air contracts (gets smaller).

YOU WILL NEED:

- **2 balloons**
- **2 empty glass bottles of the same size**
- **freezer**
- **sunny table outside**

DIRECTIONS:

1. Put one empty bottle in a freezer, and put the other empty bottle in the sun.
2. Leave them for 30 minutes.
3. Take the bottle out of the freezer and pull an empty balloon over its neck. Pull another balloon over the neck of the bottle in the sun.
4. Now, switch the two bottles. Put the cold bottle in the sun, and the warm bottle in the freezer.
5. Leave them again for 30 minutes.
6. Observe the bottle sitting in the sun. What is happening to its balloon?
7. Open the freezer and observe the other bottle. What happened to its balloon?
8. Draw your pictures below.

RESULTS:

The bottle that went from the freezer to the sun

Before sun

After sun

What I think happened to the cold air as it warmed:

_____
_____
_____
_____

The bottle that went from the sun to the freezer

Before freezer

After freezer

What I think happened to the warm air as it cooled:

_____
_____
_____
_____

Name _____

READ IT AND WEEP

Tropical storms cause people to worry because they can develop into hurricanes. You can't stop a hurricane, but you can prepare for it. Following the storm closely in newspapers and on TV can help ease fears and save lives.

To follow a storm or hurricane, you must learn to read a weather map. Like any other map, a weather map has a key which explains what the symbols mean. Here are some common weather map symbols:

SYMBOL	MEANING	SYMBOL	MEANING
H	High Pressure		Stationary Front
L	Low Pressure	○	Sunny
▽	Shower	◐	Partly Cloudy
❄	Snow	●	Cloudy
///	Rain		North Wind
	Thunderstorm		South Wind
	Cold Front	⊸	East Wind
	Warm Front		Hurricane

Use the chart above to help you read the weather map in the newspaper. Follow the weather maps for five days. Look at the place on the map where you live. List the weather forecast for your area on one day, and then the actual weather that occurred on the next day. Were the forecasts always accurate?

Date	Weather Forecast	Actual Weather	Was it Accurate?

Name _____

BUILDING A BAROMETER

Barometers measure **barometric pressure,** or how hard air pushes down. Before Hurricane _____, the barometric pressure dropped. What was the lowest barometric pressure recorded during Hurricane _____? (Check your "Hurricane Data Sheet.") _____ What is the barometric pressure where you are today? (Listen to a weather report.) _____ Compare the two readings. What do you notice?

_____

_____

_____

Low pressure in the eye of a hurricane pulls up the level of the water beneath it. When Hurricane _____ was over water (which body of water?_____), the sea level rose. Was there flooding? If so, list flood damage caused by the hurricane below.

_____

_____

_____

_____

Make your own barometer!

YOU WILL NEED:

- **aluminum pie tin**
- **water**
- **empty glass bottle**
- **ball point pen**

DIRECTIONS:

1. Use a ball point pen to draw a star in the inside bottom of the pie pan, so it looks like the picture:

Don't press too hard, or you will poke a hole in the pan!

2. Fill the pie pan half full with water. Fill the bottle two-thirds full with water.

3. Put your thumb over the top of the bottle, and turn it upside down. Lower the bottle opening below the surface of the water in the pan. Take your thumb away.

4. Slide the bottle until it is right in the middle of the pan, over the star. Balance the bottle there.

5. Mark the water level on the outside of the bottle. For the next five days, observe the water level inside the bottle, and record any changes in the table below.

6. For the next five days, also record the barometric pressure (from the weather forecast or newspaper).

Date	Water Level	Barometric Pressure

What did the water level do on days with high barometric pressure? _____

What did the water level do on days with low barometric pressure? _____

HURRICANE

MATH

Name _____

SAFFIR-SIMPSON SCALE

As you observed Hurricane _____ developing, you have recorded wind speed and barometric pressure data on your "Hurricane Data Sheet." Now use this data to rate Hurricane _____ on the Saffir-Simpson Scale from the "Hurricane Data Sheet."

Date	Wind Speed (mph)	Barometric Pressure (inches)	Saffir-Simpson Number	Notes

1. Why do scientists classify hurricanes?

_____

_____

_____

2. What do you notice about the relationship between barometric pressure and the Saffir-Simpson number?

_____

_____

_____

3. If you invented a scale and they named it after you, what would it be named?

_____

4. What would your scale measure?

_____

_____

_____

5. Describe how your scale would work, and give a few examples below.

_____

_____

_____

_____

_____

Name _____

SPIN ME AROUND

The **eye** (center) of a hurricane has low air pressure. The low pressure causes air near the hurricane to flow in toward the eye. The air movement begins to twist into a spiral. This happens because of the **Coriolis Effect,** which is a result of the Earth's rotation.

Look at the satellite pictures of Hurricane _____. Which direction did it spin, clockwise or counterclockwise? _____ Hurricanes in the Northern Hemisphere have winds that turn in one direction, while hurricanes in the Southern Hemisphere have winds that turn in the opposite direction. In which hemisphere was Hurricane _____ located? _____ Which direction would a hurricane in the other hemisphere turn? _____

Create a model of a turning hurricane!

YOU WILL NEED:

- **aluminum pie tin**
- **sheet of paper**
- **12 inches (30 cm) of string**
- **tape**
- **pencil**
- **scissors**
- **pot of hot water**
- **an adult to help you**

DIRECTIONS:

1. Draw a spiral on a sheet of paper like this:
2. Cut the spiral out.
3. Cut 12 inches (30 cm) of string.
4. Tape one end of the string to the spiral's center.
5. Have an adult helper heat water on a stove or in a microwave oven. The water should be heated until it is just about to boil.
6. Turn off the heat. Hold the spiral over the hot water by the free end of the string.

RESULTS:

Did the spiral turn? If so, which direction (clockwise or counterclockwise)?

_____

Was the air over the pan warmer, cooler, or the same temperature as the air around it?

_____

Hold this same spiral over a hot light bulb or a radiator. Describe what happens.

_____

HURRICANE
MATH

HURRICANES AND TORNADOES:
A VENN DIAGRAM

Name _____

A **Venn diagram** is a tool used to compare and contrast two different groups or items.

Try this one first! Choose a partner. Think of ways that you and your partner are the same (hair color, eye color, etc.). Write those similarities in the overlapping area between the ovals below. Now think of ways that you and your partner are different. In your circle, put words and phrases that describe only you. In your partner's circle, put words and phrases that describe only your partner.

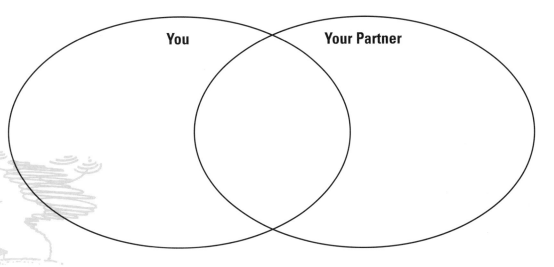

You   Your Partner

Now try a Venn diagram for tornadoes and hurricanes. Pick one hurricane and one tornado that you have studied. (This exercise is easier if you have studied both a hurricane and a tornado.) Include descriptions of: wind speed, barometric pressure, damage, or anything else you observed. The Venn diagram has been started for you.

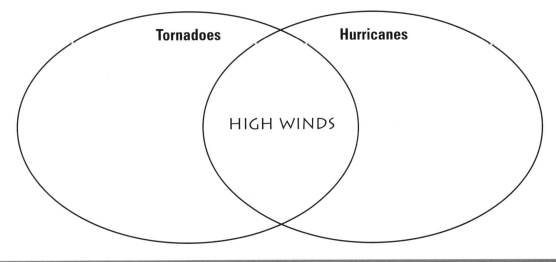

Tornadoes   Hurricanes

HIGH WINDS

Name _____

STRONGER THAN YOU THINK

As Hurricane _____ developed, what happened to the barometric (air) pressure? Did it rise, fall, or stay the same? Check your "Hurricane Data Sheet."

Write a description of what happened to the barometric pressure.

_____

_____

Why do you think this happened?

_____

_____

Air pressure drives hurricanes. Air pressure causes wind. Air pressure is the effect of all the air above you pushing down. Just because you don't "feel" it doesn't mean it's not there. Try the following experiment to see how strong air pressure can be. You might be surprised!

YOU WILL NEED:

• **thin wooden or plastic ruler**
• **a table**
• **three large sheets of newspaper, opened up**
• **a hammer (optional)**

DIRECTIONS:

1. Place the ruler so that about one-third of it sticks over the edge of a table.

2. Place three large sheets of newspaper over the ruler and smooth them down.

3. Try to make the newspapers fly up in the air. With a quick downward blow, hit the ruler with your fist or a hammer.

RESULTS:

Write about what happened:

_____

_____

_____

Why do you think this happened?

_____

_____

_____

_____

Did your ruler move? Did it break? Air pressing down on the sheets of newspaper should have kept the paper and ruler from moving. Try the experiment again with smaller pieces of newspaper. Were there any changes in your results?

© Learning Resources, Inc.

Name _____

NOT MUCH TIME

Did the residents affected by Hurricane _____ have any time to prepare? Read a newspaper story about the disaster. How were residents warned, and how much time did they have to evacuate?

_____

_____

_____

When a **hurricane watch** is issued, it means a hurricane could hit the area in the next 24-36 hours. This is the time to:

- fill the car with gas
- stock up on foods that don't need refrigeration
- fill containers with drinking water
- gather first aid supplies
- put extra lines on boats, or move boats to safer areas
- buy lumber to board up windows

When a **hurricane warning** is issued, it means that a hurricane will likely hit your area in the next 24 hours. Now you should:

- listen to the radio or TV for information
- evacuate if ordered to do so
- fill your bathtub and other containers with water
- board up windows

Imagine if you lived in the path of Hurricane _____. A hurricane watch has been issued. You must buy enough plywood to board up five windows on the east side of your house.

1. All five windows have the same measurements: 3 feet wide by 5 feet high (or 1 meter wide by 1.7 meters high). The windows are in a row, each window touching the next one, with no spaces in between. Draw a picture of the side of your home below.

[ ]

2. The plywood comes in 4 x 8-foot sheets (or 1.2 x 2.4-meters). Each sheet costs $19.51.
How many pieces would you need to buy to cover all five windows? _____ Show how you would cut, cover, and nail up the plywood over the windows on the drawing above. (Note: There is more than one "correct" way to do this.)

3. How much would this many sheets of plywood cost?
$ _____

4. What would be the least number of sheets you would need to buy to cover your 5 windows? _____
How much would this many sheets cost?
$ _____

HURRICANE WRITING

Name _____

WHAT'S WORTH SAVING?

When areas are evacuated before a hurricane, people must leave their homes in a hurry. Often they barely have time to grab a few possessions before beating the crowds to the nearest freeway.

Read newspaper reports of Hurricane _____.
When were people told to evacuate?

_____

Did people follow the evacuation order? _____

Where did the people who evacuated go?

_____

Do the articles mention what the people took with them in their cars? Perhaps they took some prized possessions that they could not bear to leave behind.

If you lived in the path of Hurricane _____ and were told that you had to evacuate immediately, what ten things (not counting people) would you take with you? List them below.

1. _____   6. _____

2. _____   7. _____

3. _____   8. _____

4. _____   9. _____

5. _____   10. _____

Compare your list with someone else in your class. Were any things on both lists? If so, list them:

_____

_____

_____

What does your list tell you about you, and what you value?

_____

_____

_____

_____

What does your classmate's list tell you about him/her?

_____

_____

_____

_____

HURRICANE WRITING

HURRICANE HUNTER

Name _____

Imagine you are the pilot on a reconnaissance flight sent to collect data on Hurricane _____. Your plane flew over, around, and through the storm. Now you must write a report to the National Hurricane Center in Miami, Florida, telling them what you observed.

Make your report as descriptive as you can. Show how you used all five of your senses as you made your observations.

Seeing:
- *what the hurricane looked like*
- *the colors of the hurricane*
- *what the ocean/land looked like*

Smelling:
- *the hurricane*
- *the airplane*

Tasting:
- *in your mouth*

Hearing:
- *sounds you heard*
- *your plane*
- *your copilot*
- *the radio*

Touching:
- *vibration in the airplane*
- *the hurricane*
- *temperature*
- *your plane*
- *wind speed changes*

TO: NATIONAL HURRICANE CENTER, MIAMI, FLORIDA

FROM:

_____

RE: HURRICANE _____

DATE: _____

REPORT:

_____

_____

_____

_____

_____

_____

_____

_____

_____

_____

_____

_____

SIGNED,

_____

WEATHER RECONNAISSANCE PILOT

HURRICANES IN HISTORY

YEAR	NAME	LANDING AT	CATEGORY	DEATHS	PRESSURE (INCHES)
1900	None	Galveston, Texas	4	6,000	27.49
1919	None	Florida Keys	4	600	27.37
1935	None	Florida Keys	5	408	26.35
1954	Hazel	North and South Carolina	4	95	27.70
1957	Audrey	SW Louisiana	4	390	27.91
1960	Donna	Eastern United States	4	50	27.46
1961	Carla	Texas	4	46	27.49
1964	Hilda	Louisiana	3	38	28.05
1965	Betsy	Florida Panhandle	3	75	27.99
1969	Camille	Louisiana, Mississippi	5	256	26.84

HURRICANE SAFETY TIPS

1. Always keep a "Hurricane Kit" handy. It should include a flashlight, extra batteries, a first aid kit, and several bottles of drinking water.

2. If a tropical storm or hurricane is headed your way, make sure your car has a full tank of gas. Meteorologists will give you enough warning to safely evacuate.

3. Tape or board up all windows. Move any loose objects, like lawn chairs and picnic tables, indoors.

4. If you are told to evacuate, do it. A hurricane warning means that a hurricane will reach your location within 24 hours.

HURRICANE GLOSSARY

barometer – an instrument used to measure barometric pressure

barometric pressure – the weight of air above a given location; cold air generally has a higher barometric pressure than warm air

Beaufort Scale – a 12-point scale used to rate wind speed

Bernoulli Effect – as air moves faster, its pressure drops

Coriolis Effect – how Earth's rotation affects weather patterns; hurricanes spin counterclockwise in the northern hemisphere and clockwise in the southern hemisphere

cyclone – a hurricane in the Indian Ocean

eye – the calm, central point of a hurricane around which the storm rotates

hurricane – a large, whirling storm of high winds and heavy rain that forms over a body of warm water; wind speeds in a hurricane are greater than 74 mph; a storm is called a hurricane only in the Atlantic Ocean; otherwise it is a typhoon or cyclone

hurricane warning – a warning issued when a tropical storm has developed wind speeds of greater than 74 mph

hurricane watch – a weather advisory issued when conditions are ripe for a hurricane to develop

latitude – the angular distance east or west of the Prime Meridian

longitude – the angular distance north or south of the Equator

Saffir-Simpson Scale – a 5-point scale used to rate a hurricane's force

tropical depression – a group of thunderstorms rotating in a spiral; wind speeds are less than 38 mph

tropical disturbance – a group of thunderstorms that have gathered together into one large group

tropical storm – a tropical depression with wind speeds between 38 and 74 mph

tropical wave – a group of unrelated thunderstorms hanging over an ocean

typhoon – a hurricane in the South Pacific

CHILDREN'S LITERATURE ON HURRICANES

- **Anderson, Lonzo. *The Day the Hurricane Happened.* New York: Charles Scribner's Sons, 1974.**

  In this children's picture book, Albie and Eldra live in the Virgin Islands on the island of St. John. When word comes of an approaching hurricane, their family prepares to ride out the storm.

- **Branley, Franklyn M. *Hurricane Watch.* New York: Thomas Y. Crowell, 1985.**

  Realistic illustrations and explanatory diagrams bring the threat of hurricanes to life, as easy-to-read text explains how and where these storms start, and what you can do to stay safe.

- **Brown, Pam. *Henry Dunant.* Milwaukee: Gareth Stevens Publishing, 1988.**

  This moving biography profiles Henry Dunant, founder of the Red Cross, the organization dedicated to helping victims of natural disasters; filled with historical photographs and drawings.

- **Gibbons, Gail. *Weather Forecasting.* New York: Four Winds Press, 1987.**

  A behind-the-scenes look at a weather station helps children understand why and how the weather changes, and how it affects our lives. Big colorful pictures and concise text make concepts easy to follow and understand.

- **Hamilton, Sue L. *Hurricane Hugo.* Minnesota: Abdo & Daughters, 1990.**

  A reporter's journal entries provide a first-hand account of the powerful hurricane that hit the Virgin Islands, Puerto Rico, and South Carolina in September 1989. This fictional report is based on fact, with black and white pictures that show the devastation.

- **Hopkins, Lee Bennett. *Weather.* New York: Harper Collins Publishers, 1994.**

  In this wonderfully illustrated book of poems, children realize the beauty of the weather through descriptive works about the sun, wind and clouds, rain and fog, and snow and ice.

- **Kahl, Jonathan D. *Storm Warning.* Minneapolis: Lerner Publications Company, 1993.**

  In this basic introduction to tornadoes and hurricanes, children learn important terminology and come to understand these natural disasters through color photographs and factual discussion.

- **Rumsey, Marian. *Hurricane!* New York: Scholastic Inc., 1977.**

  When the tide goes out and as screaming winds approach, Morgan and his dog, Tater, are stranded in a 20-foot crab boat, and must figure out how to survive.

- **Wolff, Barbara. *Evening Gray, Morning Red.* New York: Macmillan Publishing Co., Inc., 1976.**

  Learn the scientific basis behind weather folklore, as the author combines weather rhymes and sayings with explanations of why they work. Also included is a discussion of weather forecasting, and instructions for building a basic weather vane.

- **Wood, Tim. *Natural Disasters.* New York: Thomson Learning, 1993.**

  Vivid color pictures and eyewitness reports clearly illustrate the damage caused by natural disasters. Accompanying text explores history, consequences, and how man has coped with the devastating forces of hurricanes, cyclones and typhoons.